# GEORDIE SONG BOOK

## edited by Frank Graham

ISBN-13   978-0-946928-03-3
ISBN-10   0-946928-03-7
This reprint 2009

Originally published by Frank Graham
Published by Butler Publishing in 1986
©1986 Butler Publishing, Thropton, Morpeth, Northumberland NE65 7LP

**Butler**
*publishing*

# CONTENTS

# The Blaydon Races

*Air—"Brighton"*

AW went to Blaydon Races,
   'twas on the ninth of Joon,
Eiteen hundred an' sixty two,
   on a summer's efternoon,
Aw tuek the 'bus frae Balmbra's,
   an' she wis heavy laden,
Away we went alang Collingwood
   Street, that's on the road to
   Blaydon.

*Chorus:*

O lads, ye shud only seen us gannin,
We passed the foakes upon the road
   just as they wor stannin;
Thor wes lots o' lads an' lasses there,
   all wi' smiling faces,
Gan alang the Scotswood Road,
   to see the Blaydon Races.

We flew past Airmstrang's factory,
   and up to the "Robin Adair,"
Just gan doon te the railway bridge,
   the 'bus wheel flew off there.
The lasses lost their crinolines off,
   an' the veils that hide their faces.
An' aw got two black eyes an' a
   broken nose in gan te Blaydon
   Races.

*Chorus*—O lads, etc.

4

When we gat the wheel put on away we went agyen,
But them that had their noses broke, they cam' back ower hyem.
Sum went to the dispensary, an' uthers to Doctor Gibb's,
An' sum sought out the Infirmary to mend their broken ribs.

*Chorus*—O lads, etc.

Noo when we gat to Paradise thor wes bonny gam begun,
Thor wes fower-and-twenty on the 'bus, man, hoo they danced an'
    sung;
They called on me to sing a sang, aw sung them "Paddy Fagan."
Aw danced a jig an' swung my twig that day aw went to Blaydon.

*Chorus*—O lads, etc.

We flew across the Chain Bridge reet into Blaydon toon,
The bellman he was callin there — they call him Jackey Brown,
Aw saw him talkin to sum cheps, an' them he was pursuadin',
To gan an' see Geordy Ridley's concert in the Mechanics' Hall at
Blaydon.

*Chorus*—O lads, etc.

The rain it poor'd aw the day, an' myed the groon'd quite muddy,
Coffy Johnny had a white hat on — they war shootin' "whe stole the
    cuddy."
There wes spice stalls an' munkey shows, an' aud wives selling
    ciders,
An' a chep wiv a happeny roond aboot shootin' now, me boys, for
    riders.

*Chorus*—O lads, ye shud only seen us gannin, etc.

5

# CUSHIE BUTTERFIELD

*Air—"Polly Perkins"*

AW'S a broken-hearted keelman,
　　an' aw's owerheed in luv,
Wiv a yung lass in Gyetshead,
　　an aw calls her me duv;
Her nyem's Cushy Butterfield,
　　an' she sells yalla clay,
An' her cusin is a muckman,
　　an' they call him Tom Gray.

*Korus:*

She's a big lass, an' a bonny one,
　　An' she likes her beer;
An, they call her Cushy Butterfield,
　　An' aw wish she was here.

Her eyes are like two holes in a blanket burnt throo,
An' her brows in a mornin wad spyen a yung coo;
An' when aw heer her shootin "Will ye buy ony clay,"
Like a candy man's trumpet, it steels maw young hart away.

*Korus*—She's a big lass, an' a bonny one, etc.

6

Ye'll oft see hor doon at Sandgate
    when the fresh herrin cums in ;
She's like a bagfull o' sawdust
    tied roond wiv a string ;
She weers big golashes, te, an'
    her stockins was wonce white,
An' her bedgoon is a laelock,
    an' her hat's nivor strite.

*Korus*—She's a big lass,
    an' a bonny one, etc.

When aw axed her te marry me, she started te laff,
"Noo, nyen o' yor munkey tricks, for aw like ne such chaff !"
Then she start'd a bubblin, an' she roar'd like a bull,
An' the cheps i' the keel says aw'm nowt but a fyeul.

      *Korus*—She's a big lass, an' a bonny one, etc.

She says, "The chep that gets me'll
    heh te work ivry day,
An' when he cums hyem at neets
    he'll heh te gan an' seek clay ;
An' when he's away seekin't
    aw'll myek balls an' sing,
"Weel may the keel row
    that maw laddie's in !"

*Korus*—She's a big lass,
    an' a bonny one, etc.

Noo, aw heer she hes anuther chep, an' he hews at Shipcote,
If aw thowt she wad deceeve me, aw'd sure cut me throat ;
Aw'll doon the river sailin, an' sing "Aw'm afloat,"
Biddin adoo te Cushy Butterfield an' the chep at Shipcote.

      *Korus*—She's a big lass, an' a bonny one, etc.

7

# The Lambton Worm

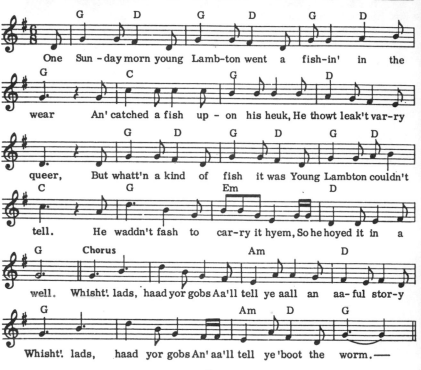

One Sun-day morn young Lamb-ton went a fish-in' in the wear An' catched a fish up-on his heuk, He thowt leak't var-ry queer, But whatt'n a kind of fish it was Young Lambton couldn't tell. He waddn't fash to car-ry it hyem, So he hoyed it in a well.

**Chorus**

Whisht! lads, haad yor gobs Aa'll tell ye aall an aa-ful stor-y Whisht! lads, haad yor gobs An' aa'll tell ye 'boot the worm.—

The story of the *Worme of Lambton* is one of the most popular traditions of County Durham. This story has been handed down by oral tradition through many centuries. The song, however, which we know today is not very old, since it was first used in a pantomime at the old Tyne Theatre in 1867.

ONE Sunday mornin' Lambton went a-fishin'
    in the Wear;
An' catched a fish upon he's heuk,
He thowt leuk't varry queer,
But whatt'n a kind ov fish it was
Young Lambton cuddent tell.
He waddn't fash te carry'd hyem,
So he hoyed it in a well.

*Chorus:*

    Whisht! lads, haad yor gobs,
    An' Aa'll tell ye aall an aaful story,
    Whisht! lads, haad yor gobs,
    An' Aa'll tell ye 'boot the worm.

Noo Lambton felt inclined te gan
An' fight i' foreign wars.
He joined a troop o' Knights that cared
For nowther woonds nor scars,
An' off he went te Palestine
Where queer things him befel,
An' varry seun forgat aboot
The queer worm i' the well.

But the worm got fat an' growed an' growed,
An' growed an aaful size;
He'd greet big teeth, a greet big gob,
An' greet big goggle eyes.
An' when at neets he craaled aboot
Te pick up bits o' news,
If he felt dry upon the road,
He milked a dozen coos.

This feorful worm wad often feed
On caalves an' lambs an' sheep,
An' swally little bairns alive
When they laid doon te sleep.
An' when he'd eaten aall he cud
An' he had had he's fill,
He craaled away an' lapped he's tail
Seven times roond Pensher Hill.

The news of this myest aaful worm
An' his queer gannins on
Seun crossed the seas, gat te the ears
Ov brave an' bowld Sor John.
So hyem he cam an' catched the beast
An' cut 'im in twe haalves,
An' that seun stopped he's eatin' bairns,
An' sheep an' lambs and caalves.

So noo ye knaa hoo aall the foaks
On byeth sides ov the Wear
Lost lots o' sheep an' lots o' sleep
An' leeved i' mortal feor.
So let's hev one te brave Sor John
That kept the bairns frae harm,
Saved coos an' caalves by myekin' haalves
O' the famis Lambton Worm.

Noo lads, Aa'll haad me gob,
That's aall Aa knaa aboot the story
Ov Sor John's clivvor job
Wi' the aaful Lambton Worm.

THE 'NEXT FOUR POPULAR SONGS BY JOE WILSON ARE REGULARLY SUNG TODAY. THEIR POPULARITY GROWS WITH THE PASSING OF THE YEARS.

Joe Wilson was one of the most successful of Tyneside songwriters. His homely songs have won him a place in the hearts of the people of Tyneside because he presented the everyday life of the working people of the area. The early years of his life are thus described in his own humorous autobiography,

LIFE O'JOE WILSON (AS IT'S GYEN). A SHORT SKETCH PUBLISHED AT THE RICKQUEST OV A FEW AUD FRINDS.

Me fethur wes a joiner an' cabinet-myeker, an' me muther a straw bonnit myeker, an' byeth natives o' the "canny aud toon o' Newcassil." Aw wes born on the 29th o' Novembor 1841, at the end o' Stowl Street, close agyen Darn Crook, an' not a hundrid miles frae Gallowgate, but *twenty minnits* efter aw had myed me forst ippeerince, te the stonishmint o' the neybors, *Wor Tom* showed his fyece, te dispute wi' me whe shud be the "pet o' the famly," an' he sweers he is te this day, *becas he's the yungist!* Aw cannet egsactly rickollect what teuk place at that remarkabil time, but aws warn'd the wimmin foaks wad heh thor drops an' cracks the syem as ivor, not forgettin te drink the hilth o' the new-born twins, an' wishin me muther seun better agyen, ivor se monny times ower.

Shortly efter wor borth, wor foaks teuk't i' thor heeds te shift te Gallowgate, an' it wes here me fethur dee'd, at the arly age o' thorty-one, leavin me muther wiv a famly o'fower, besides her-sel, te bring up the best way she cud; Tom an' me at that time not bein three eers aud. Weel can aw mind the struggils me muther had, but she work'd wiv a gud heart, an' nivor flinched frea the task afore her, her consint study bein for the gud o' her bairns.

Tom an' me wes varry young when we forst went te St. Andrew's Scheul, i' Peercy Street, where a few eers efter, for the benefit o' me-sel an' wor foaks, aw wes myed a free skollor. But Tom diddent fancy't.— It wes the forst time aw had wore different claes te him; an' it had been me muther's aim te keep us drest alike, for the likeness betwixt him an' me wes sumthin wunderful, an' the blunders it creates is varry laffabil.

At fowerteen aw went te be a printer; an' shortly efter that we left Gallowgate, the street se famous for greasy powls, legs o' mutton, sowljors, an milishamen, te leeve "farther doon the toon".

Sang-writin had lang been me hobby, an' at sivinteen me forst beuk wes publish'd. Since that time it's been me aim te hev a place i' the hearts o' the Tyneside people, wi' writin bits o' hyemly sangs aw think they'll sing. At twenty-one aw started business for me-sel as a printer, an' at twenty-two aw myed me forst success i' publishin, wi' "Wor

Geordy's Accoont o' the Greet Boat Race atwixt Chambers an' Green," It wes this eer me nyem first figor'd i' the title page o' *Charter's Comick Almanack;* an' next aw browt oot me forst number of *Tyneside Sangs.* Later on i' the syem eer aw wrote "Aw wish yor Muther wad cum," throo seein me brother-in-law nursin the bairn the time me sister wes oot, nivor dreaming at that time it wad turn oot the "hit" it did.

"The Row upon the Stairs," "The Gallowgate Lad," an' "Dinnet Clash the Door" wes me next successes ; the last one (me muther bein the subject) nearly lickin "Geordy, haud the Bairn."

Me forst perfessional ingagemint wes at Pelton i' Decembor 1864 ; me second at the Oxford Music Hall, an' me thord at the Tyne Concert Hall, Newcassil. Since then aw've been i' nearly ivry toon i' the North, an' aw's happy te say wi' the syem success aw've had i' me native place, 'aw cuddint wish for owt better, an' it'll always be me study te desarve the syem ower agyen. "May nivor warse be amang us".

Joe Wilson.

November 29th, 1867.

Joe Wilson's professional career really commenced with a three month engagement at the Oxford Music Hall, This was the famous "Wheat Sheaf" long famous as *Balmbra's.* It had passed into new ownership and the name had been changed. Joe Wilson appeared on the opening night. Thus started a period of concert life which was additional to his work as a printer. At first he worked on his own, printing his songs as he composed them. Later he had his songs printed by Howe Bros. of Gateshead where he had once worked. He enjoyed the time when he was at this Gateshead printer. We are told that *"at tea-time he used to set, not the table, but the fireside in a roar." Sitting around the fire at their teas, if the humour seized him, a trifle was enough to set him on. Anything lying about, perhaps a bill they were printing, he would take it up, and proceed in such a comic way to read it, that often their teas were never finished for laughter. His eyes, which were large, brimmed over with fun and drollery, and as he abandoned himself to the humour of the moment, voice, gesture and wit all combined to make his mock performance irresistible. One result of these outbursts of humour was that something like the following was often heard at tea-time. "Joe, aw'm not gawn te sit beside ye; aw want me tea the neet; aw'm gawn upstairs." Although thus full of live and merriment he was constitutionally weak ;and while other printers stood at their work, Joe had a seat, and laughingly excused himself by saying he could do more sitting than they could standing.*

At the height of his popularity he decided to give up the arduous concert life and settle down as a publican. He took over the Adelaide Hotel in New Bridge Street where he stayed for one year. But the life did not suit him. As he once remarked he was sadly disillusioned with his work as a landlord "if aw drink wiv iv'rybody that ask us, aw's a drunken beast; if aw dinnet, aw's a surly beast, 'awll hev to be oot on't."

His experience at the Adelaide turned him into a teetotaller and he began to compose Temperance songs which were trully based on the life of the people whom he knew so well. We have included three of them in the present work.

After a short spell as a printer he went back to the music hall but ill-health dogged him and on February 12th, 1875 he died at the age of thirty-three years.

We will conclude this short biography with two appreciations of his work. The first is from a London paper written when his career was coming to an end.

*Newcastle-upon-Tyne has always been famous for its local poets, who, in homely words and strange vernacular, reflect the passing humours of its busy population. It is a smoke-enveloped town, but the centre of immense activity; and its thousands of grimy workmen are full of fun, enterprise, and honest thought. Joe Wilson, a local poet, is one of their favourites; and no wonder, for he is a genial spirit. He knows his fellow-workmen, and is not ashamed of their lowly lot. We would not for a moment compare him with Elliot, Copper, Waugh, Barnes or Robert Burns, all of whom found inspiration in local themes; but he is a poet for all that, and, to those who can interpret the local dialect, his works afford no small pleasure.*

The second is from the Newcastle Weekly Chronicle a few days after his funeral.

*Poor Joe Wilson will be regretted by thousands of my readers, and as they sing over his "bits o' hyemly sangs" they will reflect that no common man has gone from amongst them. I don't think there are many men with such a tuneful faculty as Joe. His songs have become household words in Tyneside, and for many a mile round about. He was a good, genial, and always welcome spirit. He made you laugh until you nearly cried. He was none the worse because his talent was rough and uncultivated. He spoke to the hearts of his readers all the more readily on that account. It is a wonderful faculty that of song-writing. Only very few men have possessed it, and certainly few local poets ever had it in greater perfection than Joe; his productions are songs merely, and not poems. They don't pretend to be anything; but they are just the sort of thing for the people for whom they were written.*

# Keep yor feet still

**W**OR Geordy and Bob Johnson byeth lay i' one bed
In a little lodgin' hoose that's doon the shore.
Before he'd been an hour asleep a kick from Geordy's fut
Made him waken up te roar i'steed o' snore.

Keep yor feet still Geordy Hinney
Let's be happy for the neet
For Aa may nit be se happy thro' the day,
So give us that bit comfort keep yor feet still Geordy lad
And dinnet drive me bonny dreams away.

Aa dremt thor wes a dancin' held an'
    Mary Clark wes there
An' Aa thowt we tript it leetly on the
    floor,
An' Aa prest hor heevin' breest te mine
    when walsin' roon the room,
That's mair than Aa dor ivver de
    afore.

Ye knaa the lad she gans wi, they caall him Jimmy Green,·
Aa thowt he tried te spoil us i' wor fun,
Buy Aa dremt Aa nailed 'im hevvy, an' blacked the
    big feul's eyes,
If Aa'd slept its hard te tell what Aa wad deun.

Aa thowt Aa set hor hyem that neet;
    content we went alang,
Aa kissed hor lips a hundord times or
    mair,
An Aa wisht the road wad nivvor end,
 se happy like was Aa,
Aa cud waak a thoosand miles wi'
    Mary there.

Aa dremt Jim Green had left the toon an' left he's luv te me,
An Aa thowt the hoose wes fornished wi' the best.
An Aa dremt Aa just had left the Chorch wi' Mary be me side,
When yor clumsy feet completely spoilt the rest.

# Dinnet Clash the Door

Teun—*"Tramp, tramp."*

Oh, dinnet clash the door! aw've tell'd ye that before,
Can ye not let yor muther hev a rest?
Ye knaw she's turnin aud, an' for eers she's been se bad
That she cannet bear such noises i' the least.

*Korus.*

Then oh, lass, dinnet clash the door se,
Yor yung an' yor as thowtless as can be.
But yor muther's turning aud,
An' ye knaw she's varry bad,
An' she dissent like te hear ye clash the door.

Just see yor muther there, sittin feeble i' the chair,
It's *quiet* that she wants te myek her weel;
She's been yor nurse throo life, been yor guide i' peace an' strife,
An' her cumfort ye shud study an' shud feel!

She once wes yung an' strang, but bad health 'ill put foaks rang,
An' she cannet bear the noise that once she cud;
She's narvis as can be, an' whativor else ye de,
Ye shud study what ye think 'ill de her gud!

So dinnet clash the door, or myek ony idle stir,
For the stir 'ill only cause yor muther pain;
As quiet as can be de yor wark, an' let her see
That ye'll nivor give her causes te complain.

# The Row upon the Stairs

Teun—"*Uncle Sam.*"

Says Mistress Bell te Mistress Todd,
"Ye'd better clean the stairs !
Ye've missed yor turn for monny a
                week,
  The neybors a' did theirs !"
Says Mistress Todd te Mistress Bell,
"Aw tell ye Mistress Bell,
Ye'd better mind yor awn affairs,
  An' clean the stairs yor-sel."

*Korus.*

Oh what tungs i' the row upon the stairs,
  Clitterin, clatterin, scandal, an' clash,
    I' the row upon the stairs.


  Says Mistress Todd—"When it suits me te think that it's me turn ;
Ye've a vast o' cheek te order me, thor's not a wummin born
That keeps a cleaner hoose than me, an' mark ye, Mistress Bell,
Ef ye'd oney de the syem as me, ye'd gan an' clean—yor-sel !"


Says Mistress Bell—"Ye clarty fah, we was't that stole the beef ?"
"What de ye say ?" cries Mistress Todd, "De ye mean that aw'm a thief ?
Let's heh the sixpence that aw lent te treat Meg Smith wi' gin !
An where's the blanket that ye gat the last time ye lay in ?"


Says Mistress Bell—"Ye knaw yorfsel the sixpence's lang been paid,
An' the raggy blanket that ye lent wes ne use then ye said !"
"A raggy blanket ! Mistress Bell," cries Mistress Todd—"What cheek !
Yor dorty stockin had two holes full twice the size last week !"

"Maw holey stockins, Mistress Todd, luks better i' the street
Than yor gud man's awd blucher beuts ye weer te hide yor feet !
The eer-rings ye gat frae the Jew on tick the tuthor day,
'Ill be like the fine manadge man's shawl the syem as gien away !"


Says Mistress Todd—"Ye greet sk'yet
                                    gob
    Ye'd bettor had yor jaw,
The varry shift upon yor back
    Belongs the wife belaw !"
"Ye lazy wretch !"—shoots Mistress
                                    Bell,
    "Its true, thor is ne doot,
Last neet ye fuddled wi' Bob the Snob,
    The time yor man wes oot !"

"Oh, Mistress Bell !"—says Mistress
                                    Todd,
    "Ye brazind-luckin slut,
Ye may tawk away—te clean the stairs
    Aw'll nivor stir a fut !
Afore aw'd lift a skoorin cloot
    The mucky stairs te clean,
Aw'd see them turn as black as ye,
    Ye pawnshop-luckin queen !"

# Cum, Geordie, haud the Bairn

*Original illustrations for "Geordie, haud the Bairn"
from "Allan's Tyneside Songs," 1891.*

Teun—*"The Whusslin' Thief"*

"CUM, Geordy, haud the bairn,
  Aw's sure aw'll not stop lang;
Aw'd tyek the jewel mesel,
But really aw's not strang.
Thor's floor and coals te get,
The hoose-turns thor not deun:
So haud the bairn for fairs,
Ye've often deund for fun!"

Then Geordy held the bairn,
But sair agyen his will;
The poor bit thing wes gud,
But Geordy had ne skill:
He haddint its muther's ways
He sat both stiff an' num
Before five minutes wes past
He wish'd its muther wad cum.

His wife had scarcely gyen,
The bairn began te squall,
Wi hikin't up an' doon,
He'd let the poor thing fall.
It waddent haud its tung,
Tho' sum aud teun he'd hum,—
"Jack an' Jill went up a hill—
Aw wish yor muther wad cum!"

"What weary toil," says he,
"This nursin' bairns mun be;
A bit on'ts weel eneuf—
Aye, quite eneuf for me.
Te keep a cryin' bairn,
It may be grand te sum;
A day's wark's not as bad—
Aw wish yor muther wad cum!"

Men seldum give a thowt
Te what thor wives indure;
Aw thowt she'd nowt te de
But clean the hoose, aw's sure;
Or myek me dinner an' tea—
(It's startin' te chow its thumb:
The poor thing wants its tit,—
Aw wish yor muther wad cum!)


What a selfish world is this
Thor's nowt mair se then man:
He laffs at wummin's toil,
And winnet nurse his awn—
(It's startin' te cry agyen:
Aw see tuts throo its gum;
Maw little pet, dinnet fret—
Aw wish yor muther wad cum!)


"But kindness dis a vast;
It's ne use gettin' vext
It winnet please the bairn,
Or ease a mind perplext.
At last, it's gyen te sleep,
Me wife'll not say aw's num;
She'll think aw's a real gud nurse,
Aw wish yor muther wad cum.

# Cappy

## or, the Pitman's Dog

W. H. Dawson (1827–1879) wrote many notes to the first edition of *Allen's Tyneside Songs.* Of Cappy he wrote:

"The highwayman fellow whose bludgeon laid Cap on his back was at that time custodian of our Norman Keep, and kept watch and ward over malefactors, until the large 'stene jug' in Carliol square was finished in 1828, and made ready for their reception. He was a gross, vulgar fellow, with a 'patch on his cheek', and the name of Cappy stuck to him ever after the song appeared. Whether it was his by right before the song appeared we cannot say, but we find him so designated in a song written in February, 1826, when he was Keeper of the Castle. The circumstances that gave rise to the disaster of poor Cappy was a raid on the dogs similar to that perpetrated by the police in 1860".

The song is by William Mitford (1788–1851) and appeared in *The Budget; or, Newcastle Songster* in 1816.

I N a town near Newcassel a Pitman did dwell,
Wiv his wife nyemed Peg, a Tom Cat, and himsel ;
A Dog, called Cappy, he doated upon
Because he was left him by great Uncle Tom.

Weel bred Cappy, famous au'd Cappy,
Cappy's the Dog, Tallio, Tallio.

His tail pitcher handled, his colour jet black,
Just a foot and a half was the length of his back,
His legs seven inches frev shoulders to paws,
And his lugs like twee dockins hung ower his jaws.

Weel bred Cappy, etc.

For huntin' of vermin reet clever was he,
And the house frev a' robbers his bark was keep free ;
Cou'd byeth fetch and carry—cou'd sit on a stuil,
Or, when frisky, wad hunt water rats in a puil.

Weel bred Cappy, etc.

As Ralphy to market one morn did
  repair,
In his hat-band a pipe, and weel
  kyem'd was his hair,
Ower his arm hung a basket—thus
  onward he speels,
And enter'd Newcassel wi' Cap at his
  heels.

    Weel bred Cappy, etc.


He haddent got farther than foot o' the Side,
Before he fell in with the dog killing tribe;
When a highwayman fellow slipt round in a crack,
And a thump o' the skull laid him flat on his back.

    Down went Cappy, etc.

Now Ralphy extonished, Cap's fate did repine,
While its eyes like twee little pyerl buttons did shine;
He then spat on his hands, in a fury he grew,
Cries, 'Gad smash! but I'se hev satisfaction o' thou.'

    For knocking doon Cappy, etc.

Then this grim luiking fellow his
  bludgeon he rais'd
When Ralphy ey'd Cappy, and then
  stuid amaz'd.
But fearin' beside him he might be
  laid down,
Threw him into the basket and bang'd
  out o' town.

    Away went Cappy, etc.

He breethless gat hyem, and when lifting the sneck,
His wife exclaimed 'Ralphy, thou's suin gettin back l'
'Gettin' back' replies Ralphy 'I wish I'd ne'er gyen'
In Newcassel they're fellin' dogs, lasses and men.

       They've knocked doon Cappy, etc.

If aw gan te Newcassel when comes wor pay week,
Aw'll ken him agyen by the patch on his cheek;
Or if iver he enters wor toon wiv his stick,
We'll thump him aboot till he's black as au'd Nick.

       For killing au'd Cappy, etc.

Wiv tears in her eye Peggy heard his sad tale,
And Ralph wiv confusion and terror grew pale,
While Capp'y transactions with grief they talked o'er
He crap oot o' the basked quite brisk o' the floor.

       Weel deun Cappy, etc.

*Portrait of Tommy Armstrong from a photograph*

# Dorham Jail

Tommy Armstrong (1848–1919) was the most outstanding of miner song writers. He was a prolific balladeer but many of his songs have been lost. The following two are taken from his *Song Book of 25 Popular Songs,* third edition, 1930. The first is based on Tommy's actual experience of Durham Gaol where he was sent for stealing a pair of stockings from the Co-op at West Stanley. He says he was drunk at the time and the stockings seemed from the way they were displayed, the only pair of bowlegged ones he had come across. Being small and bowlegged they seemed ideal for him. 'Wor Nanny' is the best known of Tommy's songs because it was the only one to appear in the popular series of *Tyneside Songs* by Catcheside Warrington.

Tune: *Nee Gud Luck aboot th' Hoose*

YIL awl hev ard o' Dorham Jail,
    But it wad ye much sorprise
To see th' prisonrs in th' yard,
    Wen thay'r on exorsise.

This yard is bilt eroond we walls,
  Se noabil en see strang,
We ivor gans thae heh te bide
  Thor time, be it short or lang.

*Chorus:*

Thare's nee gud luck in Dorham Jail
  Thare's nee gud luck it awl;
Wat is breed en skilly for
  But just te muaik ye smaul?

Wen ye gan to Dorham Jail
  Thae'll find ye wiv emploi,
Thae'll dress ye up se dandy
  In a suite e cordy-roy;
Thae'll fetch e cap wivout e peek,
  En nivor axe yor size,
En, like yor suite, it's cordy-roy,
  En cums doon ower yor ies.

Th' forst munth is th' warst iv awl
  Your feelens thae will trie;
Thare's nowt but two greet lumps e wood,
  On which ye heh to lie.
Then eftor that ye get e bed,
  But it is ard is stuains;
It neet ye dorsint muaik e torn,
  For feer ye brick sum buains.

Awl kines e wark thare's ganen on
　　Upon these noable flats,
Teesin oakim, muaiken balls,
　　En weeven coco mats.
Wen ye gan in ye mae be thin,
　　But thae cin muaik ye thinnor;
If your oakim is not teased,
　　Thae'r shoor to stop yor dinnor.

Th' shoos ye get is oftin tens,
　　Th' smaulist size is nine;
Tho'r big eneuf te muaik a skiff
　　For Boyd ipon th' Tyne.
En if ye shud be caud at neets,
　　Just muaik yorsels at yem;
Lap yor clais eroond yor shoos,
　　En get inside e them.

Yil get yor meat en clais for nowt,
　　Yor hoose en firin' free;
Awl yor meet's browt te th' dor—
　　Hoo happy ye shud be!
Thor's soap en too'l, en wooden speun,
　　En e little bairne's pot;
Thae fetch yor papers ivory week
　　For ye te clean your b't.

*Spoken.*—That's th' place te gan if yor matched to fite; thaw'll fetch ye doon te yor wite if yor ower heavy. Thae feed ye on floor broth ivory meel en thae put it doon at th' frunt for e' th' hoose yor livin in. Wen th' tornkee opins th' dor, upt yor hand oot en yil get a ad iv a shot box we bee lid, en vary littil inside it; it's grand stuff for th' wumin foaks te paipor th. walls with. It sticks te yor ribs, but it's not muaid for a man this hes te yew coals. Bide eway if thae'll let ye.

# Nanny's a Maisor

## NANNY'S A MAISOR

Tune: *Peggy's Trip to Sunderland*

WOR Nan an me muaid up wor minds te gan an catch th' train,
   For te gan to th' toon te bie sum clais for wor little Billy an Jain;
But when we gat te Rowlinsgill th' mornen trane wis gone,
An thair wis ne mair te gan that way te fifteen minits te one.
So aw say te wor Nan, "Its a lang way te gan."
Aw saw biv hor fuaice she was vext;
But aw sais, "Nivor mind, we heh plenty a time,
So we'll stop an gan in we th' next."

She gav a bit smile, when aw spoak up an said :
"There's a public-hoose alang heer—
We'll gan alang thare an heh worsels warmd,
An a glas a th' best bittor beer."
Nan wis see stoot aw nue she cudint wauk,
An she didnt seem willin te trie ;
Wen aw think a th' truble aw had wiv her that day,
If aw likt aw cud brust an crie.

*Chorus:*

Ay but Nanny's a maisor she'll remane.
Is lang is aw liv a winnit forget th' day thit we lost th' trane.


So away we went te th' publick-hoose, an wen we gat te th' dor,
She sais, "We'll gan te th' parlour end," for auve nivor been in befor,
So in we went en teuk wor seets, an before aw rung th' bell
Aw axt hor what sh' was gan te drink. "Wey," sh' sais,
   "th' suaim is thesel."
So aw called for two gills a th' best bittor beer,
She pade for thim when thae cum in ;
An eftor she swalyd three-pairts iv hor gill,
She sade Bob, man, aw wid raithor heh gin.
So aw called for a class a th' best Holans gin,
An she gobild it up th' first trie ;
Sais aw te wor Nan, "Thoo's is gud is a man."
She sais, "Bob, man, aw felt very drie."
So aw called for anuthor, an that went th' suaim way ;
Aw sais, "That 'ill settle thee thorst."
She sais, "Aw've had two, an aw's nee better noo
Then aw was when aw swalyd th' forst."

She sat an drank te she gat tite ; she sais, "Man, aw feel vary queer."
"Wey," aw says, "thoo's had nine glasses a gin te maw three gills
   a beer."
She lows'd hor hat an then hor shawl, an tost them on te th' flor ;
Aw thowt she wis gan to be rang in hor mind, so a set meesel close te
   th' dor.
She sais, "Giv is order, aw'll sing a bit sang,"
Aw sat an aw gloward at hor.
Aw thowt she wis joken, for aw'd nivor heerd
Wor Nanny sing ony befor.
She gav is a tuch a "Th'. Row i' th' Guttor,"
She pleesed ivory one thit wis thare ;
Thar wis neebody in but wor Nanny an me,
An aw laft te me belly wis sair.

She tried to stand up for te sing "Th' Cat Pie,"
But she fell doon an muiad such a clattor,
She smast fower chairs an th' landlord com in,
An he said, "What th' deuce is th' matter?"

Th' landlord sais, "Is this yor wife, an whare de yea belang?
Aw sais, "It is, an she's teun a fit wi' trien te sing a bit sang."
He flung his airms aroond hor waist, an traild hor across th' flor,
An Nan, poor sowl, like a dorty hoose cat, wis tumild ootside a th' dor.
Thar she wis lyen, buaith groanen an crien,
Te clame hor aw reely thowt shem;
Aw tried for te lift hor, but aw cudint shift hor,
Aw wisht aw had Nanny at yem.
Th' paipor man said he wid give hor a ride,
So we lifted hor inte th' trap;
She wis that tite she cudint sit up,
So we fasind hor doon wiv e strap.
She cudint sit up, and she wadint lie doon,
She kickt till she broak th' convains;
She lost a nue baskit, hor hat, an hor shawl,
That mornen, throo lossen th' tranes.

# Fourpence a Day

THE ore is waiting in the tubs, the snow's upon the fell;
  Canny folk are sleeping yet but lead is reet to sell.
Come, me little washer lad, come, let's away,
We're bound down to slavery for fourpence a day.

It's early in the morning, we rise at five o'clock,
And the little slaves come to the door to knock, knock, knock.
Come, me little washer lad, come, let's away,
It's very hard to work for fourpence a day.

My father was a miner and lived down in the town;
'Twas hard work and poverty that always kept him down.
He aimed for me to go to school but brass he couldn't pay,
So I had to go to the washing rake for fourpence a day.

My mother rises out of bed with tears on her cheeks,
Puts my wallet on my shoulder which has to serve a week.
If often fills her great big heart when she unto me does say,
"I never though thou would have worked for fourpence a day."

Fourpence a day, me lad, and very hard to work
And never a pleasant look from a gruffy looking Turk.
His conscience it may fail and his heart it may give way,
Then he'll raise us our wages to ninepence a day.

# The Bonny Moor Hen

In the Market Square at Stanhope stand two inns, the 'Packhorse', once the Stanhope coach terminus, and the 'Phoenix' Hotel, built by Frederick Fenwick who used the family crest as a sign. The 'Pheonex' stands on the site of the 'Black Bull Inn' the scene of the fight known as the Battle of Stanhope.

It all started in 1797 when the Bishop of Durham issued a notice against poachers on his moors, a proclamation which was defied by the men of Weardale who considered hunting one of their immemorial rights. At last in 1818 a large body of the Bishop's men came into Weardale to arrest the best known among the poachers, boasting they "could sweep Weardale with a black pudding". Two poachers were arrested and the Bishop's men took them to the 'Black Bull' Inn. News of the arrests quickly spread, a large crowd gathered, and a fierce battle broke out. The Bishop's men were completely routed. Many keepers and constables were severely injured and the inn floor was covered with blood which one of the poachers told the landlady "to mix with meal and make black pudding of it".

The story of this affray was related in a ballad called "The Bonny Moor Hen", written, it is believed, by a local schoolmaster.

Y OU brave lads of Weardale, I pray lend an ear,
    The account of a battle you quickly shall hear,
That was fought by the miners, so well you may ken,
By claiming a right to their bonny moor hen.

Oh this bonny moor hen, as it plainly appears,
She belonged to their fathers some hundreds of years;
But the miners of Weardale are all valiant men,
They will fight till they die for their bonny moor hen.

These industrious miners that walk in their clogs,
They suit them to travel o'er mountains and bogs;
When the bonny moor hen she mounts up in the air,
They will bring her down neatly, I vow and declare.

Oh the miners in Weardale, they are bred to the game,
They level their pieces and make sure of their aim;
When the shot it goes off – Oh, the powder doth sing,
They are sure to take off, either a leg or a wing.

Now, the times being hard and provisions being dear,
The miners were starving almost we do hear;
They had nought to depend on, se well you may ken,
But to make what they could of the bonny moor hen.

There's the fat man of Oakland, and Durham the same,
Lay claim to the moors, likewise to the game;
They sent word to the miners they'd have them to ken
They would stop them from shooting the bonny moor hen.

Of these words they were carried to Weardale with speed,
Which made the poor miners to hang down their heads;
But sent then an answer, they would have them to ken,
They would fight till they died for their bonny moor hen.

When this answer it came to the gentlemen's ears,
An army was risen, it quickly appears;
Land-stewards, bum-bailiffs, and game-keepers too,
Were all ordered to Weardale to fight their way through.

A captain was wanted at the head of the clan;
H. Wye, of great Oakland was chose for their man;
Oh, his legs were too small, and not fit for the stocks,
His scalp not being hard for to suffer the knocks.

Oh, this captain he had a black bitch of his own,
That was taught by the master 'twas very well known;
By the help of his bitch he'd met many a one,
And when he comes to Weardale he'll do what he can.

"Oh," this captain says, "I am but a stranger here,
My bitch and myself is a match for a deer;
Either beggars or tinkers, she will pull off their bags,
And if that will not do she will rive them to rags.

So this army set out from high Oakland, we hear,
H. Wye in the front, and black bitch in the rear;
On they marched to Wolsingham, then made a halt,
And concerning the battle began to consult.

They heard that the miners' grand army was strong,
The captain that led them was full six feet long;
That put Mr. Wye in a bodily fear,
And back to great Oakland he wish'd for to steer.

Up spoke the game-keepers: "Cheer up, never fear,
Through Stanhope and Weardale our way we will clear;
In Durham or Oakland it shall never be said,
That by a few miners our army was paid."

So the army set off straightway, as we hear,
And the miners' grand army did quickly appear;
Oh, they fired along till their powder was done,
And then they laid on with the butt-ends of their guns.

They dismounted the riders straightway on the plain,
H. Wye and black bitch in the battle were slain;
Oh they that ran fastest got first out of town,
And away they went home with their tails hanging down.

Oh this battle was fought all in Stanhope town,
When the chimneys did reek and the soot it fell down;
Such a battle was ne'er fought in Stanhope before,
And I hope such a battle will ne'er be fought more.

Oh this bonny moor hen, she's gone oe'r the plain,
When summer comes back she'll return here again;
They will tip her so neatly, that no one'll ken
That ever they rivall'd the bonny moor hen.

Oh this bonny moor hen, she has feathers anew,
She has many fine colours, but none of them blue;
Oh the miners of Weardale, they are all valiant men,
They will fight till they die for the bonny moor hen.

*This song was first published in Frank Graham's 'Old Inns and Taverns of Durham and Northumberland' 1966.*

# The Keel Row

This popular Tyneside melody is first recorded in a *Manuscript Book of Tunes*, dated 1774, and was first published in 1793 in *The Northumbrian Garland*. It is probably the best known and most popular of Northumbrian songs. Rudyard Kipling, writing of it in India, says: "The man who has never heard the *Keel Row* rising, high and shrill, above the bustle of the regiment going past the saluting base, has something yet to hear and understand".


A S I cam' thro' Sandgate, thro' Sandgate, thro' Sandgate,

As I cam' thro' Sandgate, I heerd a lassie sing,

Weel may the keel row, the keel row, the keel row,

Weel may the keel row, that my laddie's in.


He wears a blue bonnet, blue bonnet, blue bonnet,

He wears a blue bonnet, an' a dimple in his chin;

An' weel may the keel row, the keel row, the keel row,

Weel may the keel row, that my laddie's in.

# The Washing Day

Thomas Wilson, the author of this song, was born at Gateshead Low Fell in 1773. At the age of eight he was sent down the pits as a trapper boy, and there often eighteen out of the twenty-four hours were spent in darkness sitting behind his door. To escape from this life he managed to educate himself and became a schoolmaster. With further effort he obtained a post on the Quay which eventually led to a successful career as merchant and industrialist.

His poetic career only started when he had established himself as a wealthy merchant, and his works are based on his early experiences of life. The "Pitman's Pay" is probably his best known poem. It begins:

> "I sing not here of warriors bold,
>     Of battles lost or victories won,
> Of cities sack'd or nations sold,
>     Or cruel deeds by tyrants done.
>
> I sing the pitmen's plagues and cares,
>     Their labour's hard and lowly lot,
> Their homely joys and humble fares,
>     Their pay-night o'er a foaming pot."

This leads up to a description of the varied scenes that a pay-night shows in a public-house, before the days of the teetotal movement.

"The Washing-Day" is the most popular of his homely songs.

OF a' the plagues a poor man meets
    Alang life's weary way,
There's nyen amang them a' that beats
    A rainy weshin' day;
And let that day come when it may,
    It a'ways is maw care,
Before aw break maw fast to pray
    It may be fine and fair.

### Chorus.

For it's thump! thump! souse! souse!
    Scrub! scrub away!
There's nowt but glumpin' i' the house
    Upon a weshin' day.

For sud the morn when *Sall* turns oot
  Be rainy, dark, or dull,
She cloots the bits of bairns aboot,
  And packs them off to skuel.
In iv'ry day throughout the week
  The good man hez his say,
But this, when if he chance to speak,
It's "Get oot o' maw way!"

      For it's thump, thump, etc.

Her step hez stern defiance in't,
  She luiks a' fire and tow,
A single word, like sparks frae flint,
  Wad set her iv a low;
The varry claes upon her back,
  She pinn'd and tuck'd up are,
As if they'd say to bairns and *Jack*,
  "Come near me, if you daur!"

      For it's thump, thump, etc.

The cat's the pictur o' distress,
  The kitlins daur nut play,
Poor *Pincher* niver shows his fyece
  Upon this dreary day;
The burd sits mopin' on the balk,
  Like somethin' iv a flay,
The pig's as hungry as a hawk,
  The hens lay all away.

  For it's thump, thump, etc.

The hearth is a' wi' cinders strewn,
  The floor with dirty duds,
The hoose is a' torn'd upside doon,
  When *Sall* is i' the suds:
But when the fray's a' ower an' deun,
  And a's hung up to dry,
A cup and blast o' baccy suin
  Blaws a' bad temper by.

Then the thump ! thump ! souse ! souse !
  Scrub ! scrub away !
Myek ne mair glumpin' i' the house
  Until neist weshin' day.

# Pawnshop Bleezin'

This celebrated song is written on Mrs. Trotter's Pawnshop, formerly situated in the Side, Newcastle, being entirely destroyed by fire, in the year 1849. Although a humorous composition, it faithfully describes the horrors and misery attending the use of such establishments, and is certainly one of the author's most popular productions.

WOR Sall was kaimin' oot her hair,
  An' aw was turnin' dozy,
Whiles snot'rin' in wor easy chair,
  That myeks a chep sleep cosy,
When frae the street cam screams an' cries—
Wor Sall says "Wheest!" aw rubs my eyes;
An' marcy! shoots o' "Fire!" aw hears—
Aw myeks yen lowp doon a' wor stairs,
    An' smash, aw seed a queerish seet,
    Yel thousands crooded i' the Street—
      It was the Pawnshop bleezin'.

The wimmin folks 'twas sair to see
  Lamentin' their distresses;
For many a goon, an' white shemee,
  Was burnt wi' bairns' dresses;
Peg Putty stamp'd an' cried, "Oh dear,
Wor Geordey's breeks is gyen, aw fear;
Maw bonny shawl an' Bella's frock—"
Says Betty Mills, "An' there's wor clock,
    An' a' maw bits o' laddies' claes—
    My pillowslips an' pair o'stays—
      Is in the Pawnshop bleezin'."

A dowpy wife wi' *borrow' fat*,
  An' wive puggy beak, man,
Cam pushin' wiv her bonnet flat,
  And puffin oot her cheeks, man;
Ye niver seed sic bullet eyes—
Her screams aw thowt wad splet the skies;
"Oh Lord! maw babbie's things is gyen!
Maw unborn babe hes claes noo nyen!
An' when wor Billy finds it oot,
There'll murder be, aw hae nee doot;
    O dear! what garr'd me put them in?
    'Twas a' the races an' curs'd gin—
    That set my claes a-bleezin'."

"Oh, marcy, aw'll be hammer'd tee!"
  Cries Orange Linny, blairin';
"Aw popp'd Ned's suit to hae a spree,
  But suen aw'll get me fairin',—
He thinks, poor sowl, his claes is reet,
He'll want yen suit o' Friday neet—
What mun aw dee? aw wadent care,
But, hinnies, watch an' seal is there;
    An' warse an' warse! he'll quickly
      knaw,
    That earrings, weddin' ring an' a'
      Is in the Pawnshop bleezin'?"

Lang Skipper Jack, wi' mony a sweer,
  Cam laingerin' up the Side, man,
Says he, "What's a' the matter, here?
  Noo, here's a bonny tide, man!
Why, marrows, sure it cannit be,
This isn't Trotter's place aw see?"
So oot his baccy fob he tuik,
Hawled oot some *tickets* frae a buik:
    "Why sink the sowls of a' the lot;
    Aye, d—n the yel scrape's gyen to pot,
    There's a' maw fortin bleezin'!"

The yells, an' blairs, an' curses lood,
  . And cries o' stupefaction:
An' bits o' bairns amang the crood,
  Increased the mad distraction;
Aye, mony a wife will rue the day
She put her husband's things away;
An' men will groan wi' bitter grief—
(For Pawnshop law hes ne relief)—
    To find their labour, toil, an' pain,
    To 'pear like decent foaks is vain—
      *There* a' their goods is bleezin' !


The world was better far aw'm sure,
  When Pawnshops had ne neym, man;
When poor folks could their breed procure,
  Withoot a *deed o' shyem*, man !
Ther Boxes luik like cuddies' stalls;
There's hell-fire in ther hollow balls;
Their gains is large, wor chance is sma'—
They often's get wor pledges a'—
    Just like the plagues ov Egypt sent,
    They banish peace an' calm content—
      Aw wish they a' were bleezin'.

*J. P. ROBSON*

# DI'YE KEN ELSIE MARLEY, HONEY

One of the best known of our local songs is called "Di'ye Ken Elsie Marley, honey?". This lively and spirited song was in honour of Mistress Alice Marley, the popular wife of the innkeeper of Picktree, near Chester-le-Street. The public house bore the sign of the Swan, with the appropriate motto:

> The Swan doth love the water clear,
> And so does man good ale and beer.

We are told "she was a handsome, buxom, bustling landlady, and brought good custom to the house by her civility and attention". When they passed on their way to Scotland during the Jacobite revolt of 1745 some Dutch mercenaries amused themselves by shooting at the Swan and ruined the sign. The Swan has now vanished and with it most of the old hamlet of Picktree, but the song lives on.

> Elsie Marley's grown so fine
> She cannot get up to sarve the swine,
> But lays in bed till eight or nine,
> And surely she does take her time.

> And do you ken Elsie Marley, honey?
> The wife that sells the barley, honey;
> She lost her pocket and all her money
> A back o'the bush i'the garden, honey.

> Elsie Marley is so neat,
> 'Tis hard for one to walk the street
> But every lad and lass you meet,
> Cries, do you ken Elsie Marley, honey?

> Elsie Marley wore a straw hat,
> But now she's getten a velvet cap,
> The Lambton lads mun pay for that—
> Do you ken Elsie Marley, honey?

> Elsie keeps good gin and ale
> In her house below the dale,
> Where every tradesman up and down,
> Does call and spend his half-a-crown.

> The farmers as they come that way,
> Drink with Elsie every day,
> And call the fiddler for to play,
> The tune of "Elsie Marley", honey.

The pitmen and the keelmen trim,
They drink bumbo made of gin,
And when to dance they do begin
The tune is "Elsie Marley", honey.

Those gentlemen that go so fine,
They'll treat her with a bottle of wine,
And freely will sit down and dine
Along with Elsie Marley, honey.

So to conclude these lines I've penn'd
Hoping there's none I do offend,
And thus my mery joke doth end
Concerning Elsie Marley, honey.

## DURHAM OLD WOMEN

As aw was gannin' to Durham,
  Aw met wi' three jolly brisk women;
Aw asked "what news at Durham?"
  They said—"Joyful news is coming:

"There's three sheeps' heads i' the pot,
  A peck o' peasmeal in the pudding;"
They jump'd, laugh'd, and skipp'd at that,
  For the joyful days are coming,

DURHAM OLD WOMEN.

# THE SHOEMAKKER

My mother sent me to the school, To learn to be a stocking-knitter, But I went wrang and play'd the fule, And married with a shoe-mak-ker. Shoe-mak-ker, leather cracker, With all his stinking, dir-ty wa-ter, I wish a thou-sand deaths I'd died Ere I had wed a shoemakker.

MY mother sent me to the school,
　　To learn to be a stocking-knitter,
But I went wrang and play'd the fule,
　And married with a shoemakker.

　　　Shoemakker, leather cracker,
　　　With all his stinking, dirty water,
　　　I wish a thousand deaths I'd died
　　　Ere I had wed a shoemakker.

His hands are like a cuddy's houghs,
　His face is like the high-lowed leather,
His ears are like I don't know what,
　His hair is like a bunch of heather.

　　　Shoemakker, leather cracker,
　　　Stinking kit and rotten leather,
　　　I wish a thousand deaths I had died
　　　Ere I had wed a shoemakker.

He sent me for a pint of wine,
   And I brought him a pint o' water,
But he played me as good a trick,
   He made my shoes o' rotten leather.

   Shoemakker, leather strapper,
   Three rows o' rotten leather,
   Balls o' wax and stinking water,
   Who would have a shoemakker.

# A. U. Hinny Burd.

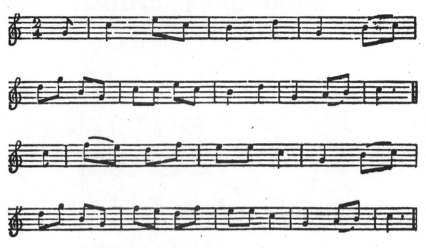

IT'S O but aw ken weel,
　A.U. hinny Burd,
The bonny lass o' Benwell,
　A.U.A.
She's lang-legg'd an' mother-like,
　A. U. hinny Burd,
See, she's rakin' up the dyke,
　A. U. A.

The Quayside for sailors,
The Castle-garth for tailors,
The Gateshead Hills for millers,
The North shore for keelers.

There's Sandgate for auld rags,
　An' Gallowgate for trolly bags:
There's Denton an' Kenton,
An' canny Lang Benton.

There's Tynemouth an' Cullercoats,
An' North Shields for sculler-boats;
There's Westoe lies iv a neuk,
An' Sooth Shields the plyece for seut.

There's Horton an' Holywell,
　An' bonny Seaton Delaval;
Hartley-pans for sailors,
An' Bedlington for nailers.

# Dance to thy Daddy

Come here, maw little Jacky,
Now aw've smok'd mi baccy,
Let's hev a bit o' cracky,
Till the boat comes in.

Dance ti' thy daddy, sing ti' thy mammy,
Dance ti' thy daddy, ti' thy mammy sing;
Thou shall hev a fishy on a little dishy,
Thou shall hev a fishy when the boat comes in.

Here's thy mother humming,
Like a canny woman;
Yonder comes thy father,
Drunk—he cannot stand.


Dance ti' thy daddy, sing ti' thy mammy,
Dance ti' thy daddy, ti' thy mammy sing;
Thou shall hev a fishy on a little dishy,
Thou shall hev a haddock when the boat comes in.


Our Tommy's always fuddling,
He's so fond of ale,
But he's kind to me,
I hope he'll never fail.


Dance ti' thy daddy, sing ti' thy mammy,
Dance ti' thy daddy, ti' thy mammy sing;
Thou shall hev a fishy on a little dishy,
Thou shall hev a bloater when the boat comes in.


I like a drop mysel',
When I can get it sly,
And thou, my bonny bairn,
Will like't as well as I.


Dance ti' thy daddy, sing ti' thy mammy,
Dance ti' thy daddy, ti' thy mammy sing;
Thou shall hev a fishy on a little dishy,
Thou shall hev a mackerel when the boat comes in.

May we get a drop,
Oft as we stand in need;
And weel may the keel row
That brings the bairns their bread.

Dance ti' thy daddy, sing ti' thy mammy,
Dance ti' thy daddy, ti' thy mammy sing;
Thou shall hev a little fishy on a little dishy,
Thou shall hev a salmon when the boat comes in.

## THE CALLER

WHY sweet slumber now disturbing,
  Why break ye the midnight peace,
Why the sons of toil perturbing,
  Have their hours of rest to cease?

    Ho! marrows, 'tis the Caller cries,
    And his voice in the gloom of the night mist dies.

The twinkling stars, thro' night shade peering,
  Blink above with heavenly light;
On the sleeping world as a voice calls clear
  In the stilly air of the sable night.

The collier sleeps, e'en now he's dreaming
  Of a pure, bright world, and lov'd ones there;
He basks in the rays of fortune beaming,
  In some far land full and fair.

Dream on thou poor and ill-used collier,
  For slaves may have visions bright;
There's One above who deems thee holier
  Than the wealthiest, in His sight.

Speed thee, old man; let him slumber
  When happy thoughts are in his breast;
Why should the world his peace encumber?
  Go! let the weary collier rest!

# The Sandgate Lass's Lament.

Tune—*"The Manchester Angel."*

I was a young maid-en tru-ly, And liv'd in Sand-gate Street, I thought to mar-ry a good man, To keep me warm at neet; Some good-like bo-dy, some bon-ny bo-dy To be with me at noon; But last I mar-ried a keel man, And my good days are done.

I Thought to marry a Parson
    To hear me say my prayers—
But I have married a Keelman
    And he kicks me down the stairs.

        *He's an ugly body, a bubbly body,*
          *An ill-faur'd ugly loon,*
        *But I have married a Keelman*
          *And my good days are done.*

I Thought to marry a Dyer
    To dye my apron blue ;
But I have married a Keelman,
    An' sair he makes me rue.

        *He's an ugly body, &c.*

I Thought to marry a Joiner
   To make me chair and stool ;
But I have married a Keelman,
   And he's a perfect fool.

                                *He's an ugly body, &c.*

I Thought to marry a Sailor
   To bring me sugar an' tea ;
But I have married a Keelman,
   And that he lets me see.

                                *He's an ugly body, &c.*

# The Keelman's reason for attending Church.

TWEE Keelmen efter leavin' Church,
    Afore me they waur walkin' ;
Close in ahint them aw did march,
    An' ower-heerd their talkin'.
Says yen, "Oh Dick ! maw heart is sair—
    Sair, sin' aw heer'd that sarmin ;
It's 'neuf to myek yen drink ne mair—
    Smash man ! it was alarmin' !

WHEN he began to talk o' Hell,
    Myed for a sinner's dwellin',
By gox ! aw tyeks it to mesell—
    It set my breest a swellin' ;
An' when he said each wicked man,
    Wad leeve alang wi' deevils ;
Aw surely thowt there aw wad gan
    For a' my former evils.

"NOO, Dick, wor ye not varry bad,
    When he sae fine was teachin' ?
Did ye not feel a' queer an' sad,
    An' trimmel at his preachin' ?

Aw's sure aw cud ha'e roar'd, Amen,
    Had it not been wor Willy ;
For he'd ha'e jeer'd an towld wor men,
    An' they'd ha'w ca'd it silly."


THEN up he spak—"Aw divvent knaw—
    Aw thowt 't was a' a folly.
Aw thowt aboot the fad a' straw,
    That Mick ga' to wor Dolly.
An' then aboot the fight aw had,
    Wi' Geordie i' the keel, man ;
Hoo aw upset him on his back,
    An' gar'd him roar an' squeel, man."


AW nobbet gan to see the Priest,
    An' hear the bonny organ ;
Aw'd seuner hev a haggish feast,
    An' drink wi' Skipper Morgan.
To tell the truth, what myeks me gan,
    Wor Maister's torn'd religious,
He'll think aw's sec a godly man,
    *And mevvies raise me wages.*


AW heer'd it just the t'other neet,
    As aw went doon the Kee man,
A chep 'at learns the folk to pray,
    Drink just as hard as me man :
Sae, Willy, if we gan to Hell,
    That Priest'll gan there tee man ;
Sae—let's away an' ha'e some yell,
    An' let sec things abee, man."

# The Collier's Rant.

A S me an' my marra was gannin' to wark,
  We met wi' the deevil, it was i' th' dark ;
Aw up wi' my pick, it being i' the neet,
Aw knock't off his horns, likewise his club-feet.

*Follow the horses, Johnny my laddie,*
  *Follow them throo, my canny lad, oh !*
*Follow the horses, Johnny my laddie,*
  *Oh laddie lye away, canny lad oh !*

AS me an' my marra was puttin' the tram,
The lowe it went oot, an' my marra gat wrang :
Ye wad ha'e laughed had ye seen the gam,
The De'il gat my marra an' aw gat the tram.

> *Follow the horses, &c.*

O MARRA ! oh, marra ! oh what dost t'u think ?
Aw've broken my bottle an' spilt a' my drink,
Aw've lost a' my shin-splints amang the big stanes,
Draw me to the shaft, it's time to gan hyem.

> *Follow the horses, &c.*

O MARRA ! oh, marra ! oh where hes t'u been ?
Drivin' the drift frae the law seam,
Drivin' the drift frae the law seam :
Ha'd up the lowe, lad ! De'il stop oot thy e'en !

> *Follow the horses, &c.*

O MARRA ! oh, marra ! this is wor pay week,
We'll get penny loaves an' drink to wor beak :
We'll fill up a bumper, and round it shall go,
Follow the horses, Johnny lad oh !

> *Follow the horses, &c.*

THEER'S my horse, an' theer's my tram ;
Twee horns full o' grease will myek her to gan,
Theer's my pit hoggars, likewise my half-shoon,
An' smash my heart, marra ! my puttin's a' deun !

> *Follow the horses, Johnny my laddie,*
> *Follow them throo, my canny lad, oh !*
> *Follow the horses, Johnny my laddie,*
> *Oh laddie lye away, canny lad oh !*

# Canny Newcastle,

## By Thomas Thompson,

'BOUT Lunnun aw'd heerd sec wonderful spokes,
　　That the streets were a' cover'd wi' guineas :
The hooses sae fine, and sec grandees the folks,
　　To them huz i' the North were but ninnies.
But aw fand meesel blonk'd when to Lunnun aw gat,
　　The folk they a' luik'd wishy-washy ;
For goold ye may howk till ye're blind as a bat,
　　An' their streets are like wors—brave and blashy.

　　　*Bout Lunnun then divvent ye mak' sec a rout,*
　　　　*There's nowse for yens winkers to dazzle ;*
　　　*For a' the fine things ye are blawin' aboot*
　　　*We can marra i' canny Newcassel.*

A Cockney chep show'd me the Thames druvey fyece,
　　Whilk, he said, was the pride o' the nation,
An' thowt at their shippin' aw'd myek a haze-gaze—
　　But aw whop't mee foot on his narration.
Wi' huz, man, three hunnerd ship sail iv a tide,
　　We think nowt on't, aw'll myek akkydavy :
Ye're a gowk if ye dinna knaw Lads o' Tyneside
　　Are the Jacks 'at myek famish wor Navy.

　　　*'Bout Lunnun, &c.*

WE went big St. Paul's an' Westminster to see,
　　An' awse warn'd ye aw thowt they luik't pretty ;
An' then we'd a keek at the Monniment tee,
　　Whilk maw friend ca'd the pearl o' the City.
Wey, hinny, says aw, we've a Shot toor sae hee,
　　That biv't ye might scraffel to heaven :
An' if on Saint Nicholas ye yence kest an e'e,
　　Ye'd crack on't as lang as ye're leevin'.

　　　'Bout Lunnun, &c.


WE trodg'd to St. James's, for theer the King lives,
　　Aw's warn'd ye a good stare we tyeuk on't :
By my faicks ! it's been built up by Adam's awn neeves,
　　For it's auld as the hills, by the leuk on't :
Shem bin ye, says aw—ye should keep the King douse,
　　Aw say see, without ony malice ;
Aw own that wor Mayor rayther wants a new hoose,
　　But then—wor Informary's a palace.

　　　'Bout Lunnun, &c.


AA hinnies ! oot cam' the King while we wor there,
　　His leuks seem'd to say—"Bairns, be happy :"
Sae, doon o' my hunkers aw set up a blare,
　　For God to presarve him frae Nappy :
For Geordie aw'd dee—for my loyalty's trig,
　　An' aw own he's a guid luikin' mannie :
But if wor Sir Mattha ye'd buss iv his wig,
　　Be gocks ! he would just luik as canny.

　　　'Bout Lunnun, &c.


AA hinnies ! aboot us the lasses did loup,
　　Thick as corrns iv a spice singin-hinnie ;
Some ahd, an some hardly flig'd ower the dowp,
　　But aw kend what they waur by their whinnie :
Aa mannie, says aw, ye ha'e mony a tite gorl,
　　An' though they're oft fine i' their trappin,

Aw'd far rayther cuddle a lass i' the *Sworl*,
    Than the dolls i' the Strand, or i' Wappin'.

      *'Bout Lunnun, &c.*

WIV a' the stravagin' aw wanted a munch,
    An' mee thropple was ready to gizen :
Sae we went tiv a yell hoose an' there gat a lunch,
    But the reck'nin, maw soul ! 't was a bizen :
Wi' huz i' the North, when aw'm wairsh i' my way,
    (But to knaw wor warm hearts ye yorsell come)
Aw lift the first latch, an' byeth man an' wife say,
    "Cruick yer hough, canny man, for ye're welcome."

      *'Bout Lunnun, &c.*

A SHILLUN aw thowt at the Play-hoose aw'd ware,
    But aw jump't there wiv heuk-fingerr'd people :
Mee pockets gat rip'd—an' aw heer'd nee mair
    Nor aw could frae Saint Nicholas' steeple.
Dang Lunnun ! wor Play-hoose aw like just as weel,
    An' wor play-folk aw's shure's quite as funny :
A shillun's worth sarves me to laugh till aw squeel,
    Nee hallion theer thrimmells mee money.

      *'Bout Lunnun, &c.*

THE loss o' the cotterels aw divvent regaird,
    For aw've getten some white-heft o' Lunnun :
Aw've learn't to prefer my awn canny calf-yaird—
    If ye catch me mair frae't—ye'll be cunnin'..
Aw knaw that the Cockneys crack rum gumshius chimes,
    Makin' gam' o' wor burr an' wor 'parel ;
But a Newcassel lad hes strung this up i' rhymes—
    Ye can sing't for a Christmas carol.

      *'Bout Lunnun then divvent ye mak' sec a rout,*
        *There's nowse for yens winkers to daxxle ;*
      *For a' the fine things ye are blawin' aboot*
        *We can marra i' canny Newcassel.*

# THE NEW GEORDIE DICTIONARY
### edited by Frank Graham

There is no definitive Geordie dialect. There are considerable variations in the speech spoken in Northumberland and Durham, partly geographical changing from north to south, partly occupational as illustrated by the mining and farming communities. The urban areas, particularly Tyneside, have also developed words and phrases with different meanings from those used in rural districts.

This dictionary uses the word Geordie in a very loose and general sense. 48 Pages and many hundred entries.

ISBN 0 946928 11 8